# CARIN THE CARER

## Nycole Lloyd

# Contents

# Acknowledgements

Could I really get away with writing a book without acknowledging the beautiful team of supporters who have had my back at every step of the way?

First and foremost, thank you to my husband Ian who is always the loudest member of my cheer squad. Babe I thank you for always being willing to push me beyond my own limitations.

Huge and heartfelt thanks to my editors, Holly Parkinson and Sheridan Ireland. Words are your forte, not mine, and I am eternally grateful to you both for making me sound smart and articulate.

To my dear friend Kellie. You gorgeous girl, are an inspiration. The warmth, kindness, compassion and humour you bring to your journey as full time carer for your beloved parents is nothing shy of amazing. I'm blessed to have you in my tribe.

# Dear Carers,

This little book is dedicated to You. It's about YOU looking after YOU.

It's for those of you who:

- Have started the journey as a carer and realised, 'holy shit', there is a LOT to this;
- Have been on the caring journey for a while and realised that you can't always carry the load yourself;
- Just need to know you are not alone;
- Want to put in place some strategies to make sure that in the book of life, you don't forget the chapter of YOU.

You're doing a great job, even if you might doubt yourself sometimes, please trust that. I really want to honour you, whoever you are. I want to honour the caring journey that you've taken on, whether that was a willing and conscious choice or just the luck of the draw.

I have a lot of respect and a lot of compassion for people who take on a caring role. It doesn't matter whether that's caring for a loved one who's at the end of their life, caring for an ageing parent, or caring for a family member or a friend who's living with a disability – huge hugs and high fives your way! I honour you!

I've done the caring role in an end of life capacity. Three times. I know what it's like to be part of a care team for someone with a terminal illness and I know that it takes more out of your heart, your body and your mind than you ever first imagined. It's one of the hardest things you can do and at the same time it can be one of the most rewarding.

Most carers fall into their role, not because they grow up wanting to be a carer, but because life's circumstances are presented in such a way that a caring role is needed. So for many reasons, people take on the job. Looking after someone you love can be an honour and a privilege. And bloody hard work...

And the emotions! So many of them, and often all at the same time. It can be pretty normal to feel like you're on an emotional roller-coaster, sometimes up and sometimes down, sometimes just stuck in limbo while other emotions get on or off the ride. And feeling all the feelings is ok, as long as we have some strategies to understand them and manage them, and not be overwhelmed or crippled (or paralysed) by them.

Please, let's acknowledge the journey that you're on as a carer. This journey isn't just about the one you're caring for; it's about the whole network of people who play a role in looking after someone. Yes, the person you care for is an extremely important part of the equation, but for this moment, this hour, this day, this book is about you. It's about acknowledging that you matter, and it's about putting your needs as a high priority on the list of things to take care of. YOU.

*Dear Carers,*

Looking after you means finding ways to care for and nurture yourself, filling your own soul and your own love tank, nurturing your being, finding space to allow you to also have a life and to have meaning and joy in your life.

I hope this book is something that helps you create a plan. It's to help you create some points of reference or some useful tools so that you don't experience burn-out or carer's overwhelm during this journey, and so you don't experience regret and resentment as part of your role.

# Chapter 1

# Self-awareness, acceptance and resilience

Before we go too far down the rabbit hole of acceptance and resilience building, let's touch on self-awareness. The dictionary describes self-awareness as *"conscious knowledge of one's own character and feelings"*, so let's start with that.

Self-awareness is a HUGE part of looking after yourself, not just within the caring journey, but in life. Having the ability to observe your thoughts, feelings, and behaviours is a great skill. Being able to use that skill to understand what's happening within yourself, in any moment, is a beautiful path to self-discovery and self-mastery.

Knowing who you are (outside of your carer role) and understanding why you do what you do can help you build resilience and assist you to move through life's circumstances with a bit more ease and grace.

We've probably all heard the saying, "It's okay to not be okay", which is a great way of saying that sometimes life throws a bit of shit at you, and you don't always have to hold yourself together when it does. You don't have to be a superhero and present the world with a happy, smiley face if that's not how you're feeling.

What's also required is acceptance: the ability to look at any situation and see it for what it is, not exaggerating it and making it bigger than it really is or trying to minimise it and make it seem smaller. Just being able to accept the reality.

To quote Byron Katie[1]

**I am a lover of what is, not because I'm a spiritual person, but because it hurts when I argue with reality.**

It's all well and good to have a deeper understanding of ourselves, and to have this well-developed sense of self-awareness, but if we're constantly wishing for things to be different and fighting what's really going on, then it's often much harder to move forward in life.

There's a wonderful quote that I love by Arthur Ashe[2], which sums up what I'm trying to say:

**Start where you are. Use what you have. Do what you can.**

---

[1] Byron Kathleen Mitchell, better known as Byron Katie (born December 6, 1942) is an American speaker and author who teaches a method of self-inquiry known as "The Work of Byron Katie", or simply as "The Work". This method helps you to identify and question any stressful thought.

[2] American professional tennis player who won three Grand Slam titles.

It's really that simple.

So, how do we connect with ourselves, elevate our self-awareness, create space for acceptance, and develop some resilience for the journey of life?

Breathe, Accept, Listen, Allow = Self-awareness & Resilience

We often underestimate the power of connecting to our breath.

Breathing is really easy, but we often do it so well and so unconsciously that we take it for granted. We generally don't even realise we're doing it.

Yet it's one of the most powerful tools available to you. The bonus is that it's simple and free.

## Just Breathe

This breathing process that I am going to introduce you to is a useful tool to help you with self-awareness and acceptance. It's about being able to stop what you're doing, connect with yourself, connect with whatever is going on within your emotions and energy, and allow your feelings to just be noticed.

1.  Identify an emotion that you're experiencing right now - any emotion is fine. Are you relaxed? Anxious? Frustrated? Impatient? Angry? Sad? Just connect with something you're feeling right now.

2. Now, put one hand on your heart and the other on your belly.

3. Take a couple of deep breaths and tell yourself what you're feeling. For example, just say to yourself, "I am frustrated right now," or "I am upset right now," or "I am angry or disappointed right now". Whatever the words are. We just want to become aware of what we're feeling.

4. Then take some more deep breaths and say it slightly differently. Use the words, "**This is what it feels like when I'm ..............**". "This is what it feels like when I'm frustrated." "This is what it feels like when I'm upset." "This is what it feels like when I'm angry or disappointed."

This process helps you acknowledge and understand that these are the feelings you are experiencing in your body. This is also how it shows up in your thoughts and in your behaviours. You might notice different sensations in different areas of your body, or your attention might be drawn somewhere in particular. Just observe what's going on for you.

Obviously, you can practise this when you are feeling a variety of different emotions. It's a good way to build yourself some reference points and to understand how you react to different situations in your life. *Not all emotions are going to feel the same way.*

# Now Accept

There's nothing to do with those feelings or thoughts. They don't need to be fixed. They don't have to be changed. It's not right or wrong; just accept that when you're frustrated this is how it feels within your body, or this is what it's like when you're angry. This is how it shows up in your body, your mind, your energy. This is 'what is'.

There's amazing power in that: to just stand quietly with your hands on your chest and belly, and allow yourself to acknowledge what's going on within your body – to allow the truth of what's happening right now.

Sometimes you'll find that the words will change by this simple act of acknowledgment. You might start off by saying, "This is how it feels when I'm angry," but just naturally it might change to be, "This is how it feels when I'm hurt," because on some level, you're realising what the real cause is beneath the surface emotions.

When you can be still long enough and accept whatever is going on, you can often find a whole new level of self-awareness. This then becomes a stronger foundation on which you can move forward.

Also give yourself permission to let go of the thoughts and feelings that arose. You don't need to hang onto those emotions (unless you really want to) once you have the insights they provided. Part of moving forward is being willing to release what is in the past, particularly if it is no longer helpful to you.

**The next step** is about being able to support yourself regardless of what emotions you're experiencing and being able to provide yourself with what you need. This is about developing resilience.

So, what is resilience?

*Resilience is the ability to 'bounce back' from stressful or challenging experiences. It involves being able to adapt to changes and approach negative events, sources of stress, and traumatic events as constructively as possible.*[3]

Being resilient doesn't mean you won't ever experience difficult life events, but rather that you're better prepared to cope with them when they do occur.

# And listen

Remember that emotion you were working with earlier?

Okay, so again, put one hand on your heart and one on your belly. Take a deep breath and check in with yourself by saying, "Hey, it's okay (babe, hun, sweetheart* insert your term of endearment of choice), I'm here for you. What do you need? What do you want? How can I support you?".

---

[3] Mental Health Association, NSW

It might feel a bit awkward having a little chat to yourself but hang in there. This process is really about connecting back to you. Asking these questions is about connecting with all of you – your mind, your body and your energy/spirit – to acknowledge that in this moment whatever you're feeling is ok.

And when you're asking, "What do I need?", it's important to be still and to LISTEN. Allow yourself time to connect with your intuition or your gut, or whatever you want to rely on, to HEAR what's being said. This is about you, so trust yourself. You might need nothing – simply witnessing yourself and your emotions could be all you require. However, it could also be that something else is required, for example perhaps asking for support from someone within your care network.

## Allow yourself to receive

Please note, this isn't about changing the external! If your thoughts are, "I need the person I'm caring for to change," then please go back and ask yourself again, "What do I need?". Sure, you might want other people to change, but that's something you may have no control over so it may not happen. What you're looking for are insights into what will support you and what you can give yourself to feel calm and whole and okay.

Once you 'hear' or 'know' what you need to support yourself right now then it's important to take action on that. Whether it is something you can gift yourself or some support you require from an outside source, allowing yourself to receive this much needed support will complete the care loop.

If you aren't used to sitting quietly with your own thoughts (in meditation or yoga or something similar) you may need to allow yourself some time. Be gentle on yourself if nothing comes up immediately. You might find that you have an 'aha' moment after the fact and then you can use the information when it arises, rather than trying to force something to occur now.

As an example, let's say that you're frustrated with the day because it's been challenging and emotionally tough. You've just found a few moments to be still and to breathe and acknowledge that this is how it feels when you're frustrated. You can feel the tension in your neck and jaw, and you feel as though you want to cry. Take another breath and tell yourself, "It's ok, I'm here". Ask yourself, "What do I need?".

The first answer in your head is, "I need them (the ones I care for) to let me help them get dressed. They can't do it on their own"... Hmm, that's an external reference, so let's ask again, "Hun, what do you need right now?". You take a breath and listen.... And you get the feeling that you need to be acknowledged; you need someone to acknowledge that you're doing your best right now. So, give that to yourself.

Sitting there, hand on heart, hand on belly, take some deep breaths and say to yourself, "You're doing a good job right now. Yep, it's tough and sometimes it's even harder when the people you love and care for stubbornly push you away because they are trying to maintain their independence, but you're doing great. You're hanging in there and I can see you're frustrated, and yet I see you're also doing your best. I see you and I acknowledge all that you're doing."

You take some more breaths, relaxing your body, and you also realise that you could benefit from some time out. So that might be something to arrange for yourself

When you use this Breathe, Accept, Listen, and Allow technique, it creates space for your heart and your mind to ask the body what it needs. I feel that's one of the things we often forget in the journey of building resilience and finding acceptance. We forget to check in with our body and our energy/spirit.

Often the belief of, "It's okay not to be okay," is very mind-driven. While I really honour the strength of the mind, and I like practical and pragmatic solutions to things, we can sometimes neglect what's going on in our cellular body. It's important to look after ALL of you and to try not to overlook any elements of yourself. Your mind, your heart, your physical well-being, your spirit/energy – they're all in this together.

That's step one as a carer; it's about how to you stay connected to you.

It's important to acknowledge, "This is how I feel when…" whatever's going on. Then you can also acknowledge, "It's okay, I'm here for you. What do you need?" You may not have answers to those questions; it's just about creating space. This is about allowing you (your energy or spirit or just some unconscious part of you) to know that it's supported, and witnessed, in whatever it's experiencing.

Then remember, you have permission to just let it all go.

# Chapter 2

# You and Them... Not You for Them

At the risk of sounding a little like Marie Kondo[4],

**What sparks joy in your life?**

What lights you up? Do you love watching nature documentaries? Do you enjoy gardening? Maybe you're a keen Mine Craft fan? Perhaps golf is your thing? Do you even know what you like doing when you have time to yourself?

It can be really easy to lose track of who you are when life gets busy. Hey, it happens to all of us. You fill life up with things to do, right? Whether it's just working, raising a family, or being a carer, you can end up with a life full of 'to do' lists. You get focussed on the next thing that needs your attention and put your time and efforts into getting the items crossed off your list. Often you forget to add 'look after me' to that list. You can end up treating yourself like a well-functioning and very capable

---

[4] Marie Kondo is a tidying expert, bestselling author, star of Netflix's hit show, "Tidying Up With Marie Kondo," and founder of KonMari Media, Inc.

human machine, and subconsciously decide that you will give it attention IF and WHEN something goes wrong. The very things you did to become this wonderful capable human often get neglected. But they are the very things you need to STAY well-functioning and capable.

STOP! Before you go off on a tangent and berate yourself for any neglectful self-behaviours, I want you to know that I forgive you and I want you to forgive yourself too. You're doing an amazing job and I didn't raise these issues so you could have something to feel bad about. I mentioned it so that we can have an honest conversation about your needs and about including things into your life that continue to nurture and support you. That's it.

I also know that time is a very precious commodity and you don't always have nearly enough of it. So, let's explore how you could use your time in ways that don't always involve ticking things off a 'need to get shit done' list.

If it's been a while since you had any time to yourself, to do something just for you, it's quite possible that you've forgotten what it feels like. I can't tell you how many times I've asked a carer what they like doing in their down time and their response was like a deer in a headlight. They don't even know how to answer that question anymore because it's been too long since the idea of doing something for the pure enjoyment of it was even an option.
Well it's time for a change.

**Time for a little self-reflection and some self-discovery.**

Before you go any further you are going to need some supplies.

I suggest you grab a pen and paper, or a journal or notebook. You're going to spend a little time on this so if you can grab yourself a cup of tea or a glass of wine, that might also be helpful and a little enjoyable. ☺

1. Write down how much time you get to yourself each day, or each week. Be honest. I know it's possibly not the same each day or each week, but if you were to have a think about your average week, where are the pockets of time?

2. How long are these pockets of time in which you would get to do something of your own choosing?

3. When you do get to have this time to yourself, do you find that you know exactly how you are going to spend it?

*If you already have a list of things that you would participate in during your free time, then you might want to skip along to the next chapter. Feel free to hang around and possibly get some new ideas, but if you're already good at incorporating the things that bring you joy, relaxation, and nurturing then perhaps you can put down the book for a bit and enjoy some 'you time'.*

However, if 'time to yourself' leaves you feeling lost and wandering in circles, feeling like you just don't know what to do with yourself… then let's continue.

Now is your chance to explore some ideas and take a moment to create yourself a quick reference guide. You're going to create a list of joy-filled, relaxing and nurturing ideas that cater to your specific wants and needs.

Get comfortable and take some deep breaths. Feel yourself relaxing a little more within your body. Feel your feet upon the ground, wiggle your toes a bit to get a good sensation in your feet.

Take a few moments to allow your mind to drift through thoughts, ideas, or images of things that you enjoy. Just let it flow.…

If you need some ideas to get you started: Do you like art? Perhaps reading? Maybe you enjoy being active – gardening, exercising, walking? Do you like creative projects and making things? Do you enjoy mentally challenging pursuits like jigsaw puzzles and crosswords?

What is it that helps you to connect back to yourself? What is it that enables you to feel nurtured and relaxed? What are the things that make you smile and brings a sense of joy and fun into your life?

*insert thinking music of your choice here.

Now, write down all those things that made you feel good. All the ideas that came to mind, no matter how small or how large, write them all down.

The next step is to categorise all the ideas you had. Think of it this way:

- If you only had 20 minutes to yourself, which of those things on your list could you do?
- What if you had 40 minutes to yourself?
- What things on your list could you indulge in if you had one to two hours at your disposal?
- If you had half a day, or even better a full day??

If you need to work within a budget, then add that in too. Give yourself some options from 'absolutely free' to 'hey big spender' (whatever that is within your financial realm).

You might end up with something like this:

|  | 20 min | 40 min | 1 hour | 2 hours | Half day |
|---|---|---|---|---|---|
| $ | Enjoy a cup of tea in the garden | Take the dog to the park for a walk | Get out the sketch pad and draw | Sort out old photos | Go for a bush walk |
| $ | Do a short meditation | Bake something yummy | Sleep / power nap | Go for a bike ride | Spend time at a local art gallery |
| $$ | Enjoy an extravagant chocolate or treat | Go buy some new plants for the garden | Head to the gym | Walk to the coffee shop for a treat | Lunch and shopping with friends |
| $$$ |  |  | Enjoy a deluxe pedicure | Indulge in a relaxing massage | Adventure – sky dive or balloon ride |

Please remember to be honest with yourself. I've given you examples of what I might like to do, but if you genuinely find that cleaning or ironing is relaxing, put that on your list. Whatever you like to do is perfect.

This journey is about you and what works for you, nobody else gets a say in what 'should' be on this list.

Don't make this a list of all the things you feel you 'need' to do. (That list is already long enough thank you very much.) This exercise is to help you get back in touch with the things that you enjoy and to assist you to find ways, no matter how big or how small, to incorporate a bit of joy into your days.

It's important to remember that this is about what lights you up. What makes you feel relaxed and nurtured? What are the activities that help you feel engaged in the world so that you can feel empowered to bring your A-game to being a carer?

# Chapter 3

# Practical ideas to develop support networks

Life is a team sport, and I believe it's an absolute requirement that you build a team around you who love you and can hold and support you, both physically and emotionally. As a carer, I think having support networks is absolutely, utterly imperative.

When I talk about building support networks, I'm talking about You, not the person you're caring for. I'm not talking about the health professionals and the carers and the connections that you need for whoever it is you're caring for – whether it's a palliative care team, or a medical professional, or the aged care agencies – I'm talking about who supports you. A lot of the 'professional care team' (as mentioned above) are built for the person you're caring for, and yes, there's a component of what they do that will include you and support you, but how do you develop networks that support you personally?

Remember, this book is for you to look after <u>YOU</u>.

Your networks consist of some professionals, as well as your family and friends. These break into three strong groups of supporters.

## Network #1 – Your team of Specialists.

This is about the team of people that provides paid specialist support; any service that helps you feel good about yourself.

If you were an elite athlete, you'd build a team of professionals around you to support you for your sporting events. As a carer, think of it like running a marathon. This is not a sprint, there's a long-term journey in front of you. And so, start (or continue) developing a team who is going to support you. It could include a nutritionist or a massage therapist, or it could be independent counsellors or psychologists; heck it could even be the beauty therapist or the hairdresser. And it definitely includes any not-for-profit organisations, such as the carers' organisations that you can phone to talk to someone for advice.

## Network #2 – The pragmatic and practical support team.

Let's class one group of family and friends as your 'practical pragmatic supporters'. They are the 'get shit done' people. They're the ones you could hand a mop and a bucket to and ask, "Can you mop my house," and they wouldn't even bat an eyelid, they would just get it done. These are the friends who you know you can call and say, "I've run out of milk and bread, is there any chance you can go to the shop for me, because I can't get there today." These are the family and friends who, when they come to visit, will walk in the door and say, "Can I help you?" And if you respond with a request to hang out the washing for you, they don't say, "Oh no, that wasn't what I was thinking". They say, "Absolutely, where's the basket?". These people go on your practical list.

## Network #3 – The emotional support team.

The other group of people are more your strong emotional supporters. They're the "I need to have a cup of tea with someone who can just hear me out" people. They're the someone who can just hold space for you while you rave and rant and vent. Sometimes the people on your practical list are the same people on your emotional support list, and sometimes they're not. On this list are those people you're okay to have a good laugh and a good cry with, and you feel so much better afterwards, even if they didn't do anything except have a cup of tea with you. Sometimes your practical support people aren't so good at the emotional stuff; they want to do things, they want to take action, they want to be given a task. That's fantastic. Your emotional supporters are less likely to want to be given a task, but for whatever reason they are just so great at holding your heart when you need it.

Let's do some exercise. (Promise you won't even break a sweat.)

Get three pieces of paper. You are going to create three lists, so label each piece of paper accordingly:

1. Your specialist helpers: nutritionists, psychologists, a good pedicure person.

2. Your practical, pragmatic supporters; your "get things done" people.

3. Your emotional support team; your "loads of hugs and laughs" people.

For your first list, your professional helpers, just go ahead and write down all those people you pay for specialist services. You probably already have a good idea in your head of who they are, but it can help you to feel well looked after just to see that list in writing.

For the second and third lists, think about your family and friends and write down their names under the most appropriate heading. Decide whether you think they would be good as either a practical supporter or an emotional supporter (or both if you feel that would be the case).

Let me be clear. It doesn't matter that you just love your cousin and that she'll be quite upset if she doesn't make it onto a list. If she's unreliable and you end up being more of a support to her than she is to you, don't put her on the list. This list is about the people you know and love, and the people who will most likely be there for you. This is not about keeping people happy at the expense of yourself.

**How to harness your teams.**

Before you start work on activating your teams, I'd like you to do one more thing.

Write down all the tasks, jobs and activities that are a part of your carer's life. In particular, put a mark against the ones you would happily delegate or accept help with.

This does not have to be a definitive list. It's just a good start to identify what you do and where some team support could benefit you. It can be very helpful to have a quick reference when people ask "what can I do"?

Now that you've got a list of tasks and those three network lists, let's work out how to put them to good use.

Network #1.
This is one of the easier networks to engage. When you know you need help you pick up the phone and make an appointment. Pretty simple huh? Since you're paying them for their time and expertise, and you know what support they can offer you, probably the most negotiating you'll need to do is about finding an available time for you both.

Networks #2 and #3.
It's great that you have now identified people on your support teams; however, it works best if they also know that they're on

your team. So, the next step here is to get in contact with the people on your lists.

Make time to contact each person and let them know you'd like them to be on your team. My suggestion would be, if you have some people on the practical support list, ring them and say something like, "Hey, I've been doing this exercise where I identify my support networks, and I've put your name down as someone who would be there for practical support, should I need it."

Then ask them the following three questions.
A. "Are you okay to be on my list?"
B. "Can I call on you when I need help?"
C. "Do we need to put any boundaries in place?".

For starters, these three questions let people know that you're thinking ahead; you've given them a heads up that you might call on them for help if and when you need it. You're also managing people's expectations (yours and theirs). It helps to tell them which list you have them in, and this can also help you confirm that that's the most suitable role for them (you can change the list they're on if you both decide that's a better option). It'll also let them know in what capacity you might be calling. This is also where your quick reference task list comes in handy (just in case people want ideas of how help looks to you).

Secondly, these questions give your loved ones and friends permission to say yes or no. As mentioned above, it helps expectation management when people have the option to agree or decline whether to be involved. It allows them the choice to be there. In my experience, people are keen and willing to step up and support other people, but often they don't know how to. They don't know what would be useful and what would be intrusive, and they'll sometimes wait until they get a clue or an instruction from you before they take action. It's really good to let them know that yes, they'll be called upon if they've agreed to that.

**But what if they say no?** When you're asking someone if they'll be on your team, please remember that you've given them permission to decline if that's right for them. Hey, they may be sorting out their own issues and not have the time, ability or emotional capacity to help you, and that's okay too. Don't take that as a reflection of your friendship, just politely leave them off your lists.

Thirdly, putting boundaries in place helps set the scene. It allows everyone to have clarity on what's expected and gives people guidelines to work with. For some people, being there for you requires its own set of logistics. If you're ringing a girlfriend at three o'clock in the afternoon when she's picking her kids up from school, she might not be available to help you. If you're relying on her to be there, you both might be disappointed that she isn't available. Discussing boundaries allows you to determine when and how it's going to work. Some people will say, "Call me any time", but others will say, "I work Mondays and Tuesdays, but any other day of the week I'm free to be there for you". Some will say "call me if you want me to make extra meals for you, but I'm no good with ironing". Each to their own.

All this pre-emptive planning, along with phone calls and discussions with family and friends, is there to help you. Believe me, it will make your life easier knowing that you have networks of people who have your back.

It's not uncommon for carers, or anyone really, to feel awkward and uncomfortable asking for help. We live in a time within society when being self-reliant is held in high esteem, so it's not surprising that we've forgotten the idea of sharing the load. I hear it all the time, "Oh, it's probably easier if I just do it myself", or "I don't want to burden anyone else", or "what if they think I'm not doing a good job if I ask for help?".

Can we please agree, here and now, that you are willing to drop the old stories and embrace a new one? The new story is simply this

**We don't have to do all of it alone.**
**We were never meant to.**[5]

---

[5] Brene Brown is a research professor at the University of Houston and author. She has spent her career studying courage, vulnerability, shame, and empathy.

# Chapter 4
# The Emotional Scorecard

Don't panic, this isn't a judgement of your emotional performance. This is, however, a very simple system that was developed to help you check in with yourself and articulate where you are on the spectrum of 'okayness'. Really, it's about how you're doing.

This is a way to observe your thoughts, your feelings, your behaviours – when it's all good, when you're going off track, and then when it's really bad for you. It can be a useful tool to help identify what your triggers are, when you need to rely on the support systems that we've discussed, and how you de-escalate the issues causing you most concern.

This system helps you to better identify how an imbalance in your internal emotions shows up in your body, your mind, and your behaviours. This whole system is based on regular traffic lights, or traffic signals, that you see when you're out driving a car or at other intersections.

The Emotional Scorecard looks like this:

Green Zone – It's All Good
In terms of your emotional spectrum, the Green means you're going along fine; you're able to respond to life and the changing environment. It means you're coping well. You're in control of your life; you're eating well, you're participating in the things that bring you joy, you're sleeping well, and you feel as though your stress levels are low. All the things that feel good.

Amber Zone – Caution Ahead
In the Amber Zone, things are probably not so good and you may have shifted within your 'okayness' spectrum.

It can be a warning that if you continue along this path then you could be heading for trouble. You can still take corrective action here, and this is the area where if you're not aware what's going on then you might get into trouble, but if you work out what you need to do (for yourself or with the help of others) then you can stay safe and emotionally okay.

Red Zone - Stop
The Red Zone is usually a sign that you need to stop. Something is definitely not okay.

This is when you're not coping, and you need to take immediate action. Generally, by this stage you're going to need help from outside sources, whether that's your friends and family or professionals around you, but, generally, assistance is going to be required.

Let's consider this from the perspective of having a known and manageable medical condition.

For example, if you know that you have diabetes then you know what it feels like when everything is healthy and well and your blood sugar is balanced. You know how it feels in your body when it's in the Green Zone.

If you haven't eaten for a while and your blood sugar drops, you would know the signs and symptoms of that. You might feel confused or dizzy, and you might start to feel a little shaky. This is what you would call the Amber Zone. When you start to feel unwell, you know there are steps that need to be taken in order to change your blood sugar levels. Whether that's eating food, taking medication, drinking water, or actually stopping and sitting down and resting, you would know what steps you need to take in order to halt the progression of the blood sugar issues.

If you don't take corrective action in this Amber Zone, you are heading towards potential trouble. This is the Red Zone. For a diabetic, you might experience sweating, chills and weakness. Now, this would definitely mean getting outside help. You would want someone to ring an ambulance and possibly get you to hospital. This is the, 'You've tipped over the edge and you are really in trouble now' area.

Most people who are living with a medical condition have learnt how to manage it. They understand what it feels like in each of those areas: when it's all good, when there's warning signs, and when to stop.

In the emotional scorecard system, it's not too dissimilar. The main difference is, for most of us, you don't always have clear indicators; you don't always see the signs and symptoms quite so easily. This is why it's good to develop some useful observational skills and self-awareness by learning to look out for your thoughts, feelings, and behaviours.

Remember section one, when you did the breathing exercises? Those exercises are a great tool to help you connect with yourself and check in on how you are doing.

To help develop your observation and awareness skills there are three types of questions to ask in each of the different zones:

1.  Thoughts - What is going on in your mind? What kind of thoughts are you thinking?

2.  Body - What's going on in your body? How is it feeling?

3.  Behaviours - How do you treat yourself and others? How do you act towards or react to people and circumstances?

Let me give you some examples.

**GREEN**

1. When you're in the Green Zone, what's your natural style of thinking? You might be thinking, 'Hey, I've got this. This is a challenging job that I've taken on, but I'm really proud of myself for what we've managed to achieve so far. I'm really honoured that I'm able to look after my parents".

2. In terms of what is going on in the body, what feels 'normal' and comfortable? You might be smiling and be feeling energised. You would probably feel healthy and well, getting plenty of sleep, and generally feeling good.

3. When you look at how you would be treating yourself and others how does that show up? You might feel that you are creating opportunities to enjoy the things you love. You would be eating well and looking after your physical and mental health. Most likely your self-talk is positive and you're patient and helpful to those around you. You treat yourself and others with respect.

**AMBER**

1. In the Amber Zone your thoughts could be more like, "I'm not sure that I can do this, this is more challenging than I thought". Often this is where you start to have doubts and concerns creep in. For example, "I don't know if this is the right decision I've made. I've got all

this information and it's really hard to discern which is the right answer". Those thoughts might feed back into what's happening in your body.

2. You may feel sick and anxious about things. When you observe what's happening in your body you might be getting really tired, or your thinking might become foggy. It could be that you don't feel as well or you're not getting enough good quality sleep. You might take on more responsibilities than necessary in order to prove to yourself that you've got this.

3. In that Amber Zone, if you ask yourself, "How am I treating myself and others?", you might find that you have stopped looking after yourself as well. For example, you may be staying up a bit later at night or eating too much sugar. You might be a little less patient with other people instead of really taking the time to help them with something – it could be eating a meal or getting dressed – and you find yourself getting a little bit snappy with them.

**RED**

1. In the Red Zone, you are usually so much harder on yourself and others. Often, your thoughts are more critical or harsh than when you are in the Green or Amber Zones. You might think, "I'm such an idiot, how could I forget that?", or, "This is all too hard for me. I don't think I can do this". They're very 'brick

wall' kind of thoughts; you're not open to ideas and problem-solving attitudes, and you're thinking very closed-down statements to yourself.

2. When you consider what is happening in your body, this is often when you might start to get sick. You hardly ever spend time doing what you enjoy, and your stress levels are escalating.

3. You might be existing on hardly any sleep and feel anxious more regularly than not. When you are here in the Red Zone you are often quick to criticise yourself and others, and kindness, patience, and helpfulness has gone out the window!

These are just examples and may not necessarily be true for everybody. The key is to ask yourself these questions at each stage of the process. You can use these three areas of thoughts, body, and behaviours to help stay observant to what is going on within yourself.

If you need, go back to the first section of this book and get more familiar with the tools to Breathe, Accept, Listen, and Allow.

Like many things, these skills of self-awareness will take time to develop. The more you can practise observing your behaviours and asking yourself these questions, the easier it becomes to notice what the patterns are around your thoughts, feelings, and behaviours. It can take weeks or even months to get to the stage where observing yourself from moment to moment seems quite effortless and normal. One day you could feel you're in the Red Zone, the next day could be totally Green. It's okay. It's all about observing, noticing, and learning to adjust accordingly.

Self-Question Time.

My recommendation is that you do these questioning exercises when you're in a good frame of mind. It's generally easier to sit and consider your answers when your mind is clear and your emotions are calm. From this place you can think about different times in your life that might fit into each of the criteria for each 'Zone'.

Oh, please grab yourself a pen and paper, or your journal. You will want to take some notes here.

Draw three columns – one for green, one for amber, one for red. See where I'm going here?

Before we start with some exploration, sit down and think about times in your life when
    a) things have been good,
    b) life has been challenging or not-so-great yet still man-ageable, and
    c) life has been absolutely terrible.

These will be representative of your Green, Amber, and Red Zone days.

Now, you're going to spend some time identifying how you feel in each of those areas.

## It's all good.

Think about a time when everything was going well and you felt really good about the day. Have a think about how you felt within yourself: how did your body feel? How did your spirits feel? How did your emotions feel? What sort of thoughts were you having? Was your mind clear? Were you in a problem-solving mode? What sort of self-talk did you hear yourself saying? What sort of words did you hear yourself saying when you were talking to others? How did you treat yourself and others? What sort of food did you put in your body? What sort of relaxation things did you do? What did you do for others without being requested, just because you were feeling great about the world? That's in your Green column.

## Caution Ahead.

For your Amber column, consider a time when things started to unravel a little. Maybe something unexpected happened in your caring world. Maybe a new medical issue developed or there was a last-minute change of appointment that you needed to adjust; maybe something was not quite right with plans and processes. Take yourself to a time when things just didn't go so well. What was happening then? How did you feel? What was happening in your body? What was your energy like? What were your emotions like? What kind of thoughts were you thinking? Do you recall the kind of things about the day, the situation, the things that didn't go so well, and do you find that you start using victim statements? What sort of thoughts come up? And on an amber day, how do you treat yourself and others? It could be that you go, "I'm too busy, I can't go for a walk for myself today," or, "It's too hard to make nice, healthy food. I'm just going to have takeaway". What are the things that you do when you're under pressure and things are not going well?

## Stop.

Now for your Red Zone, your stop zone. Think about a day when things really went to shit. Maybe you were caring for someone and they ended up in hospital unexpectedly. Maybe you had three other appointments on the same day, and you tried to manage everything. Think about what happened on a day like that. What was happening in your body? How did you feel energetically? How did you feel emotionally? Did you find that you felt nauseous, or did you find that you had headaches? What was going on in your body when this was happening? What kind of thoughts were you thinking? On a day like that, when there are a lot of things going wrong, you might find that you're a person who goes into hyper-fix mode, where you try to micromanage every element of life.

Maybe not. Are you trying to control every little section of the day, or is it more the, "Oh… panic stations ahead!" When you're in this Red Zone, how do you treat yourself and others? Is this the kind of place where you snap at other people, or do you just shut down and stop communicating with people completely?

Take some time now to write down your reflections from the above exercise.

Take all the time you need.

~~~~~~~~~~~

Is it painting a picture for you? When you sit back and reflect on the work you've done, identifying your thoughts, feelings, and behaviours in each zone, can you identify any patterns emerging? And to the best of your ability, without judgement, are you understanding yourself a little better? It can be interesting to take note of how your thoughts, feelings and behaviours can change (or not change) with different levels of stress and chaos.

It doesn't matter if you're asking yourself these questions once a day, three times a day, or seven times a day. It's really just about the self-awareness we talked about earlier. Think about what's happening in your body, thoughts, emotions, and behaviours.

From here, there's only one more step.

## Triggers and support mechanisms

As I discussed earlier in this book, self-awareness (being able to observe your own patterns of thoughts and behaviours) is a skill that's important to develop. Even better is using these skills to help you develop resilience for the road ahead. Self-awareness can help you identify what pushes you from the Green Zone up to Amber and Red. Then, how can you use this knowledge to help de-escalate yourself back down from Red, to Amber, to Green?

Consider your previous scenarios, the ones you thought about over the last page or so, and particularly focus on the Amber and Red Zones.

Can you identify what your triggers were? What specifically occurred that changed your mood or your level of coping? These are the triggers. Do you remember what was happening just before the time you felt were Amber or Red? What were the things that occurred to escalate you from being 'okay' to 'I need help'? Was it a particular incident or just a general building up of stress?

Once you've identified your triggers, take note. This will help you get a clearer picture of what can upset your balance, and you can use this information to work out what you need, or need to do, to bring yourself back to a place of capable resilience.

It goes without saying that sometimes the reason for a change in your Emotional Scorecard will be things beyond your control. It could be other people's behaviour, or external circumstances (like traffic or the weather) that will have influence over how your day changes. Unfortunately, you can't always change the external forces that are involved in your life. Yes, they concern you and can impact your day and your mood, but spending too much time (and effort) on trying to change things you have no control over can leave you totally exhausted. That's not our goal here; we're trying to look after you.

My suggestion, without writing you a whole new book, is that you do your best to stay focussed on the issues that you do have control over. You can stay in charge of your decisions and behaviours and continue to practise the tools you have. Take time to Breathe, Accept, Listen, and Allow, so you can take a step back, observe the situation, and determine what you need to support you.

**I am not a product of my circumstances.**
**I am a product of my decisions.[6]**

So, what can you do to support yourself? Do you need to make time to do something nice for yourself? What can you do that is nurturing and caring? Who can you call upon within your networks when you need help? What help do you need?

---

[6] Stephen Covey, American educator, author and businessman. His most popular book is *The 7 Habits of Highly Effective People.*

What would support you and help change your thoughts, feelings, and behaviours to take you from that Red Zone (and hopefully you don't get there too often), back to Amber and Green.

What's beautiful about all these observations and learnings is that they don't have to stop with you. It can be very helpful and a great learning curve to work through the Emotional Scorecard with those you are caring for. That way, you both have insights into what it looks like when it's all good, or caution is required, or you desperately need help.

You can create some simple flags and clear communication that will help you both to look out for each other. Use this simple Emotional Scorecard system to create support strategies that work for you both.

I would even encourage you to share your insights with others in your close networks (if you are comfortable doing so). The more people you have looking out for you and supporting you, the easier it becomes to notice when you need caring for. Sometimes you just can't see what's happening to yourself because it's too close for comfort, and you're distracted with being in it rather than observing it. *This is not about opening yourself up for unjust criticism, but rather for allowing others to gently mention if they think you seem to be struggling emotionally.*

Let me share a personal story with you.

For me, when I'm moving from the Green, 'all is good', to the Amber, 'caution ahead', zone, I start cleaning the kitchen. (Who knows why it's the kitchen of all places.) I get really pedantic about cleaning, and every crumb and little bit of mess will drive me nuts.

When I'm in the Green Zone, I just like the kitchen to be regular clean, you know?

But by now I know, and my family knows, that if I start cleaning the kitchen like a crazed ninja then something is up! This is the first sign that I'm not coping with something or that I'm starting to feel out of control with an issue in my life. If I notice this pattern taking place (or if they do and it gets pointed out), then I step back and take myself off somewhere quiet to work out what's really going on for me. I breathe, I connect, and I check in with what I need.

When I've cleaned the kitchen two or three times in one day, we're starting to go beyond the 'caution ahead' Amber Zone and we're heading towards the Red 'stop' Zone. It may be that I've overstepped my own warning signs, and I'm heading for some kind of emotional meltdown, which is NOT going to be pretty (for me or for anyone else).

That is one of the little things that I have observed in myself, and that my family confirm I do. The kitchen thing…

The reason I share this with you is just to illustrate how you can identify what is happening to you at each stage of the traffic light.

# That's a wrap...

Now it's time to move forward, keep caring for those you love, AND keep looking after You.

The tools and techniques we've discussed through this book are yours to play with. Keep working with them. Keep practising and refining them. Put them to use.

Remember, you're doing a great job! Even if it doesn't feel easy or graceful, you're looking after someone you love. It's a tough job but it can also be rewarding.

Sometimes, when you're knee deep in the day-to-day requirements of being a carer, it's easy to forget about who you are without this role. Your willingness to take on the role of carer for someone is an amazingly generous task. I hope you can find time to celebrate the journey and to celebrate YOU along the way.

I also hope that you've learnt a little about yourself while reading this book.

To refresh your memory – just in case you've been busy caring for your loved ones and your thoughts have been otherwise occupied – this is what we covered:

1. You have a process you can use to:
   - Breathe and connect with yourself and see how you are doing;
   - Accept what is happening within;
   - Listen to what you need to support yourself; and
   - Allow yourself to be supported.

2. You've created an easy reference guide of activities you can engage in for the pure joy of it. This list can be revisited again and again. You can update it as often as you need and be as playful as you like with what you include. Don't be afraid to change it as needed - dispose of the things that are no longer fun or nurturing. This is YOUR list so it's up to you what goes on there.

3. You've created a list of your support networks (Specialists, Practical, and Emotional Supporters) who will be there, ready and willing, to assist you. You've also put some thought into how to activate them and when to use them. By the way, I understand that you probably have plenty of things to take care of, so telling your family and friends how to be of support to you can feel like **another** task. Rather than thinking of it as something you have to do for them, please remember this is about *setting yourself up for success* and being clear with your support networks about what they can

do to help. Life's a team sport, don't forget you have other members on your team, let them know what positions they can play.

4. I've also introduced you to the Emotional Scorecard, a system that encourages you to use your thoughts, your body, and your behaviours to gauge how you are doing. Use this as often as you need to check in with yourself. Ultimately, any practise that you undertake to help expand your level of self-awareness will be beneficial to you and to your wellbeing. The Emotional Scorecard is just one method, and I encourage you to keep exploring others that you come across in life.

Please remind yourself (daily, if needed) that you aren't broken, you don't need fixing, and you don't need saving. This book was never about that. It was written simply to give you some additional tools and support to make the caring journey a bit easier.

*That's a wrap...*

Now that you've read the book, and hopefully had a chance to implement some of the strategies, I'd love to hear from you.

Please email me at info@livinglovingdying.com

I'd love to get your feedback and hear how the strategies and processes in the book have made a difference in your life.

And if you need some help getting your thought together, perhaps these questions might help you get started.

- How has this book helped you as a carer?
- What did you find was the easiest tool to implement?
- Was anything I suggested not very helpful?
- Did anything trigger you emotionally? And if so, are you willing to tell me what that was?
- Was there anything you would want to learn more about that I didn't cover in this book?

With gratitude and thanks,
**Nycole**

# Author Bio

Nycole Lloyd -Founder of Living, Loving, Dying, is a trained end-of-life consultant.

She is passionate about her work which involves providing support and guidance on several levels, regardless of age or health condition, to people at this very delicate stage of their life. Knowing what paperwork would be best to have in place, the right questions to ask and what they need to look for in regards to end-of-life issues can provide a sense of peace and relief.

She assists the dying and their loved ones to understand how to support each other and grieve. Nycole is committed to improving end-of-life literacy and discussions around death.

Nycole is a big believer in helping people to remember that they are truly alive until they have taken their last breath. So until that time comes, she encourages people with the aspects of living a full life, that has meaning to them, now!

Nycole is a member of the International Institute for Complementary Therapies and fully qualified as an End-of-Life Doula and a Strategic Intervention Coach. Her educational background in Counselling and work in hospice support, as well as her own personal experience being a loved one's carer, has given her a base from which to approach many topics relating to caring, grief and death. She is passionately interested in the connection between mind, body and spirit. Nycole is a Spirit of Light Practitioner and has over 15 years experience in energy healing and transformation processes.

Nycole specialises in: Family and carer support; grief and bereavement support; end-of-life education; doula services; funeral services as well as other end-of-life services.

Read more: https://livinglovingdying.com/ or facebook.com/LivingLovingDying/.

Lightning Source UK Ltd.
Milton Keynes UK
UKHW022341281220
375969UK00007B/297